Harnham Mill

Sarum Studies 2

Michael Cowan

the oldest surviving paper mill in the country

First published in the United Kingdom in 2008, on behalf of the Sarum Chronicle Editorial Team,
by The Hobnob Press, PO Box 1838, East Knoyle, Salisbury SP3 6FA.
© Michael Cowan 2008

British Library Cataloguing in Publication Data
A catalogue record for this book is available from the British Library.

ISBN 978-0-946418-67-1
Typeset in 11/13 pt Octavian. Typesetting and origination by John Chandler
Printed in Great Britain by Salisbury Printing Company Ltd, Salisbury

Contents

Harnham Mill: a Chronology

about 1135
there may have been a watermill on this site as early as the mid 12th century, probably a corn mill

1299
a documentary source refers to a 'fulling' mill operated by the Pynnocks where newly woven cloth was pounded by wooden hammers to compact the fibres – Salisbury's medieval cloth industry was developing vigorously at this time

1425
the Pynocks still fulling

about 1500 to 1550
the long low stone building was built in the early part of the 16th century, essentially the building still to be seen, as a paper mill with the characteristic features of fireplaces, unglazed windows and apertures
Salisbury was a very large city by the standards of the time and a new market for paper was emerging

1714
by this date industrial paper making had put the mill out of business and it had reverted to fulling

between 1810 and 1834
the four storey brick building was constructed as a yarn factory equipped with carding machines to clean and teaze the wool, and spinning jennies to create the yarn

about 1840
the mill had become a bone mill, grinding animal bones for fertilizer, and the yarn factory was still operating

1879
the mill was let to a tallow chandler, making and selling cheap candles, still in business in 1931 when the building was sold

1938
by now a hotel and restaurant

Introduction

MOST WATERMILLS, when their active days are over, either fall down and disappear or, if attractively sited, are converted into desirable residences. The mill at West Harnham near Salisbury has been fortunate to remain working well into the twentieth century and to have survived only slightly altered as The Old Mill Hotel. There are but few documentary clues to its story over possibly nine hundred years. This short work endeavours to lay out the chronology, to describe the various manufacturing processes that took place at different times and to set the mill in its historical and geographical context. Locally it is universally known simply as 'the old mill'.

In medieval times the mill played a role in the local cloth industry. From the sixteenth century it was part of the developing paper industry. It continued through the nineteenth century and into the twentieth with the more mundane activities of making bone meal and tallow candles. The published documentary evidence is scant but enough to create what I trust will be regarded as a tempting picture. There is undoubtedly more to be discovered – but that is for others.

One really important uncertainty is the exact date of the present stone building. The answer with the greatest authority published by RCHM(E) in 1980 tells us that it 'appears from the style of the architectural ornament to have been built c.1500'. There is present day endorsement of this by Tim Tatton-Brown, Salisbury Cathedral archaeologist and acknowledged specialist in medieval stonework. His assessment is 'early Tudor between 1490 and 1510'. This is much earlier than other paper mills noted in the literature; they were built later in the sixteenth century with one exception. A mill near Hertford was 'set up by John Tate in the 1490's'[1] but apparently

1   Shorter (1966) p 5

did not last long. Nothing of it survives but given that it existed there could have been others. In 1500 Salisbury was a very large city and it may not be surprising that a demand for paper should be met, as early as that, by local production.

I have many to thank for help and support, and often pointing me in the right direction. Locally, Alan Lovering at his restored and working Ford Mill provided an understanding of mill machinery, and Tim Tatton-Brown advised me on stonework. Nationally I am grateful for advice from Simon Hudson of the Mills Section of the Society for the Protection of Ancient Buildings; from Ron Cookson of the Mills Archives Trust.; and particularly for the interest and expertise of Martin Watts, specialist and prolific author on mills. Similarly the work of John Vince has been invaluable, and an example of the calligraphy and drawing in his Sorbus books is used for Fig 8 illustrating fulling-stocks. Charles Villiers took most of the photographs of the mill creating an important record of much that has remained unchanged since Tudor times.

It has been of inestimable value to have had the enthusiastic co-operation of Simon Hemington and Steve Thomas, owners of The Old Mill Hotel. Hadrian Cook provided the superb interior shot of the roof – a most important feature because dendrochronological analysis of the timber would give the building a more precise date. I am grateful to Jane Howells and Sue Johnson for finding interesting material that I had missed. The latter produced the intriguing fact that in 1938 the Old Mill Restaurant and Hotel was the headquarters of the Salisbury branch of the English Folk Cooking Association – specialising in Wiltshire dishes. And of course no list of thanks for any local work would be complete without acknowledging assistance from Bruce Purvis and his staff at Salisbury Local Studies Library.

Finally my thanks to John Chandler of Hobnob Press and the Editorial Team of *Sarum Chronicle* for publishing this work as part of their new co-operative venture. John also pointed me towards Charles Singer's 1950s multi-volume *Oxford History of Technology*, from which, with the agreement of the Clarendon Press, many of the illustrations have been gathered. I was saddened to discover in my most recent consultation that it had been retired to the nether regions of the library, available on request but not publicly shelved. For anyone interested in the sort of activities carried on over the centuries at Harnham Mill it is still a delight.

Historical research can seldom be regarded as certain and it is a risky matter to assert something too strongly. Nevertheless the sub title of this work remains 'the oldest surviving paper mill in the country'. Let others challenge that if they can!

Michael Cowan, October 2007

1
Nine Centuries

A neighbour good, a miller too
And yet an honest man

epitaph at Longbridge Deverill, Wiltshire

early views

HARNHAM MILL is built across a leat drawn from the southern arm of the River Nadder where the river divides around some of the water meadows in the parishes of West Harnham and Britford, Salisbury (SU136294). The first known illustration of the building is the watercolour by John Buckler painted in 1803 and reproduced on the back cover.

When considering what has happened at and to West Harnham mill over perhaps the last nine hundred years it is fortunate that the Reverend Peter Hall, curate of St Edmund's Church, had time on his hands during the early part of the nineteenth century. He was able to produce fine drawings, published in 1834 as *Picturesque memorials of Salisbury*. It is equally valuable to us that the Harnham Women's Institute unearthed important clues in 1954, but we will return to them later.[2] The earlier Buckler work was part of a Wiltshire-wide commission by Sir Richard Colt Hoare for his library at Stourhead and is recognizable as the building still there. The tall adjacent brick building does not appear in this watercolour (although it does show a single storey stone extension to the west) but is in Hall's 1834 engraving.

2   See pages 10 and 12

1 The Reverend Peter Hall's view of the mill in Picturesque memorials of Salisbury, a series of original etchings and vignettes ......etc 1834

Hall's drawing (his Plate VIII reproduced as Figure 1), from the north bank of the River Nadder looking south west, shows clearly what is still there today. On the right, behind a high wooden fence is the cottage now known as Island Cottage, of undated origin and much changed but old enough to have been shown on the 1787 Inclosure map. A wide pathway between it and the mill leads to a wooden bridge crossing the southern arm of the River Nadder above a weir and past the site where Rose Cottage would later be built in the 1840s. The path then continues on a causeway beside Longbridge Lane, across the water meadows to the northern arm of the Nadder at Long Bridge and Fisherton. A man in a billy-cock hat, carrying a basket, has come from that direction and is just passing a blocked up doorway. Numerous ducks were to be seen there in the 1830s as they are today.

The pathway in front of the mill was wide enough for a two wheeled cart to be loaded. Was it backed into position from the far, south bank over the wooden bridge, or, even more perilously, turned in front of the building? The modern footpath is just wide enough to turn such a vehicle. If it had come from Salisbury and Fisherton it would have entered the ford just out of the picture to the right but, instead of crossing to the south bank, could probably have turned up the alternative exit behind the ducks, accounting for the lie of the land that still remains.

The long low building was almost certainly built as a paper mill 'about 1500' although that date has to be strongly qualified and a more detailed discussion of the probabilities appears elsewhere.[3] Today it is often referred to as a 'delightful and picturesque old [insert century to taste] mill' with a somewhat dismissive 'together with the Victorian warehouse'. The two disparate structures are now in combined use as The Old Mill Hotel. The tale of what has happened over the centuries can be recovered quite fully from a handful of published sources, together with simply looking at the building from the twin archaeological and architectural points of view.

A great deal of mythology, not unusually, comes with such a tale. Notwithstanding the excellence of his drawing the Rev Hall's caption (of its time remember — 1834) now perhaps leaves something to be desired.

> Of this remarkable interesting pile, the upper story of the principle front, together with the roofing, and the whole of the square premises beyond, are of modern introduction. The rest bears evident testimony to the reigns of Henry the 7th or 8th [1485 to 1547]. By many persons it is supposed to have been attached to some ancient grange, or farm; but more probable conjecture assigns it originally to the Dean and Chapter of the Cathedral. The style of building betrays a remarkable admixture of the domestic with the castellated of an earlier date; while a niche, in the upper story of the northern gable, imparts the additional character of devotional sanctity and retirement.

He must mean one or other of the east or west gables; the latter is now masked by the later building and from evidence inside the building both gables are exactly the same. His sense of direction may have been weak but his dating is spot on. The Royal Commission on Historical Monuments (England), naturally hedging its bets, says in its 1980 volume on Salisbury that Harnham Mill (Building 588) 'appears from the style of its architectural ornament to have been built c1500'. Dendrochronology to determine the date of the roof timbers would settle the matter if funds permitted.

But do we see in Hall's caption the genesis of the story that the building, c1500, housed the 'cathedral muniments' while the new cathedral was being built (albeit 250 years earlier)? This tale has appeared several times in recent years on the publicity boards outside the hotel. Does it also account for the 'tradition' reported by the Harnham W I in 1954 that 'it was used as a hostel for the nuns of Wilton Abbey, when their own dwelling was being 'sweetened'?

3   See pages 5, 11-12

fulling

ULLING WAS AND IS part of the process of making cloth and is explained in a later section.[4] So when was this fulling mill first built and why? The ladies of the WI in their short but usefully informative 1954 booklet *A history of Harnham* provide the date 1135 for the mill's first existence. They quote no source but presumably had a reason, although this may have been nothing more than myth. 1135 is totally unproven, but at least credible. There are more provable records. Firstly, a negative – there is no Domesday Book reference in 1086. Sometime in the next two hundred years a mill appears, described in 1299 as a 'freehold fulling mill'. This reference is to be found in the authoritative work *Wiltshire and Somerset woollen mills* by Kenneth Rogers, quoting Wilts.Inqp.p.m.1242-1326.[5]

He does not name the occupant but a later reference provides it – Pynnok. This occurs in a national survey *Medieval English Clothmaking* by AR Bridbury who cites PRO [now TNA] CP40/453/181d to quote: 'The Pynnoks who ran a fulling mill at Harnham on the southern outskirts of Salisbury in 1299 were still in possession in 1374'.[6]

There are also four indexed references to Pynnok (or Pinnock) in the 1420s in *The First General Entry Book of the City of Salisbury 1387-1452* which mainly records meetings of the mayor's court and lists of citizens.[7] The one of particular interest names those who were to deal with claims on the lands and tenements in West Harnham of the late John Pynnock in 1425, thus taking the occupancy to a period of at least 125 years.

Rogers also identifies fulling mills at Winterbourne Ford [sic] on the River Bourne in 1372, referred to in 1399; at Barford St Martin, on the River Nadder in 1410[8]; and for completeness, at Leigh near Westbury, 25 miles from Salisbury. Other such mills in the area, identified by John Chandler in *Endless Street: a history of Salisbury and its people* are at

2 Medieval fulling tub, French stained glass 1460 (Singer vol II p 216)

4 See page 21
5 Rogers p 227
6 Bridbury p 65 note 40
7 Carr (ed) Wiltshire Record Society Vol 54 2001, entry 247
8 Rogers p 253

Stratford sub Castle, Milford, Mumworth [near to the modern Petersfinger], and Town Mill.[9] They were all part of the dominant cloth industry in and around a burgeoning New Sarum – by 1377 the seventh largest city in the kingdom. Harnham Mill's relatively rare freehold status meant that it was not an 'adjunct' to the manor and was free to trade in its own right.

paper

THE PRESENT MILL, which it has to be assumed is on the same site, was built about 1500, but bear in mind that this is a judgement

3 *Paper stamping machine; the hammers are lifted and then dropped into the long tub from tappets on the drive shaft (see also Figure 9); notice, on the right, how water is conveyed to the tub. Harnham Mill was still a paper mill at this time and, estimating its size, machinery of this nature could have been installed there. (From* Bockler *Theatrum Machinarum Novum 1662 in Shorter, plate B: reproduced with the permission of the Science Museum/ Science and Society Picture Library)*

9   Chandler 1983 p 292 note 12

on the basis of building style. It was and is a handsome (and for its time expensive) stone and flint building. Stylistically everything points to it being a paper mill, a change of use consistent with the decline of the cloth industry[10] and a newly developing market for paper. How it may have operated is discussed in a later section.[11] It appears to have remained in use as a paper mill for some two centuries until local paper making began to decline. The 1954 WI history refers to a 'deed of assignment' dated 18 Jan 1700. No source is provided for this document but such a precise date suggests that it exists, and a published quotation makes it credible (incidentally providing a good sense of the paper making process): 'on that date it was leased by William Turner of Bemerton to Richard Long of New Sarum, including the 'wheels, shaft stockes [timber supports for the troughs], hammers troughs and all other things belonging to the milling or beating of stuffe to make paper.'[12]

fulling again

I T MAY BE that the machinery was listed for sale as paper production was to cease. Certainly by 1714 there is a record in the Court of Common Pleas in London of: 'a recovery suffered upon *inter alia* a grist and two fulling-mills in Fisherton and West Harnham.'[13]

A recovery was a legal process to remove an entail, or restriction on the property and no doubt could be a pretty lengthy process. Fisherton is the parish to the north of Harnham, beyond the northern arm of the River Nadder and the grist, or corn, mill was doubtless on the site of the eighteenth century mill demolished in the mid twentieth century. The two fulling mills were at Harnham and Bemerton – both in the parish of West Harnham.

Richard Long, the leaseholder in 1700 was a man of substance and had become Mayor of New Sarum in 1697. According to local tradition the name 'Long Bridge' dates from that time. Long would have been a been an astute businessman able to see that a local small scale production of paper was being pushed out by centralized factory production using larger machinery developed on the continent. He appears to have taken the mill back to fulling cloth. Salisbury's cloth industry had declined but never disappeared and underwent a revival between 1780 and 1810.

10   Chandler 1983 p 92 and Purvis 2003 p 50
11   See Chapter 3
12   Harnham Women's Institute 1954 p 10
13   Victoria History of Wiltshire (VCH) volume 6 p187 note 42

4 An earlier published
version of this photo-
graph is captioned
'Walking cloth in tubs,
Connemara. This was
the original method of
fulling throughout
Britain before the
introduction of the
fulling mill'. The length
of cloth is drawn from
the basket on the right
and successively through
all four tubs (Pelham,
plate 1: originally from
'Early cloth fulling and
its machinery', by E
Kilburn Scott in
Transactions of the
Newcomen Society 12
(1933) pp 31-52)

A variety of later documentary references about Harnham Mill between 1754 and 1844 are recorded by Rogers.[14] In 1753 Harnham Mill was insured for £200 by a Salisbury clothier, Joseph Champion, confirming that by then paper had indeed given way to the return of cloth. An apparently unrelated occurrence was that Harcourt Bridge [in what is now Mill Road, Fisherton]: 'formerly a footbridge [beside a ford], was rebuilt in stone in 1777 at the expense of the parish. The cost was thus borne on the understanding that the owner of Harnham Mill would keep the bridge repaired thereafter. The owner's responsibility was transferred to the parish in 1801.'[15]

Possibly the Harnham owner, who might, twenty five years on, still be Joseph Champion, or more likely a successor, thought the cost worthwhile because a bridge made transporting the 'says' or lengths of cloth from the city weavers and then, after fulling, back to the 'tenterers', that much easier. However there were still fords to be negotiated across both arms of the Nadder. Maybe it was just philanthropy? Or a public relations exercise knowing that if the agreement was for a fixed period not a lot would would need to be done to a new stone bridge in the 24 years before the parish took the cost back? The answer to this question probably lies in the city records.

The West Harnham Inclosure map of 1787 shows Martin Neave as the owner of both Harnham and Fisherton mills. In 1799 Harnham was offered for sale as a 'fulling mill of six stocks [more than the two or

---

14   Rogers pp 254-5
15   VCH 6 p 181, citing Sarum Corporation papers

three commonly recorded] occupied by Samuel Williams, in full trade and capable of improvement for a "manufactory"'.

This improvement appears not to have been carried out as it was still only a fulling mill, let to Thomas Lucas, when it was again for sale in 1810. Ownership passed, with Fisherton Anger Mill, to Stephen Bell and John Sutton. The two mills remained in joint ownership until 1931. A small 'factory' was built between the 1810 sale and Hall's picture in 1834; the four storey brick building now the guest accommodation part of the Old Mill Hotel. The Bell and Sutton business may not have lasted long, judging by the sale recorded in 1818, but activity seems to have continued for some time. The 1834 Tithe Commutation Act document describes Harnham as having a 'tucking' (fulling) mill, although by this time Salisbury's cloth industry was fading.

yarn

THE 1818 SALE identifies the 'manufactuary' as a yarn factory and included 'a scribbling engine, two carding engines, nine jennies and two billies'. In operating sequence, the scribbling engine provided the first rough cleaning and disentangling of the wool fibres; the carding engines refined this process. A 'slubbing billy' pieced together and lightly twisted the short lengths of fibre from the carding machines. The lengths were the 'slubbing' ready to be spun by the 'jennies'. The Spinning Jenny was simply an 'engine', a multi spindle spinning machine invented by James Hargreaves in 1764. Although still a domestic machine, it began the process that would revolutionize the wool and cotton industries, and result in the great mills of the north. Little wonder perhaps that a valiant but relatively tiny business in Salisbury did not survive much longer.

Nine spinning jennies in the four storey factory and six fulling stocks taking the ground floor space of the mill next door was, in local terms, impressive but in the wider context of a developing industry, perhaps not sustainable. The machines were tiny compared to the water powered goliaths of places like Cromford Mill in Derbyshire. Fulling stocks, now in Leeds Industrial Museum, are taller than the men who fed in the cloth. The intact structure of both buildings at Harnham makes it clear that, while the fulling was water powered, the yarn factory machines were manually operated. The initial and finishing stages of cloth manufacture were gathered together, but not apparently the weaving itself. But of course the absence of looms from the quoted sale list does not actually exclude the unlikely possibility that they were there.

The clothier in 1818 was John Batchelor. Between 1832 and 1846 the factory was let by Bell and Sutton to Alexander Minty and 'so survived in the trade longer than any other near Salisbury'.[16] Fifteen hands were employed in 1838. In 1844 it was described as a yarn factory occupied by Alexander Minty of Castle Street, Salisbury, yarn factor.

bones

AT SOME STAGE water-powered fulling in the mill must have ceased and it was recorded as a bone mill by 1840. Bones were crushed for fertilizer but this too had ended by 25 April 1879. A single page contract was signed on that date and now hangs in the hotel restaurant. It has been summarised as follows:

> a James Sangar rents the eastern part of the ground floor from Henry George Gregory. A condition was that Sangar was to remove 'the present bone crushing machinery consisting of rollers and flywheel and stands'. He was also to 'erect partitions and doors to lock on each side of the wooden casing of the water wheel', could widen a door at the back and could install a copper [a cooking or laundry boiler] 'under the present chimney breast.[17]

Mr Gregory had purchased the mill and other properties [for £7,690] in 1848 after a bankruptcy sale.[18]

tallow

THIS BONE CRUSHING machinery referred to in the contract of 1879 was to be removed at the end of the tenancy together with other 'trade fixings'. On the document there is a plan

16 Rogers p 255
17 Cowan 2005 page 98
18 *Salisbury Journal* April 1 1848 p 4

5 Part of the ground floor south front of Harnham Mill in 2006; one of the two windows with a wave moulded hollow chamfered and roll moulded stringcourse. This part has been extensively repaired in earlier times before modern conservation techniques were developed. The window has protective iron bars sealed into the stone with lead; glazing was a later addition. (photograph Charles Villiers)

of the ground floor showing the machinery to be taken out, superimposed in Figure 18 on the ground plan drawn by the RCHM(E). A later sale in 1931 made it clear that a Mr Sangar was still in the tallow business; perhaps it was the same James Sangar as in 1879 but after 52 years probably not. In the mid-1920s a Mrs Emily Sangar is listed in local directories as a tallow merchant at the Bone Mill.[19]

Water power was no longer needed, so no doubt the waterwheel disappeared at an early stage but the four fireplaces must have been invaluable. The processes are described later.[20] Without this use continuing well into the twentieth century it would have been easy for the building simply to perish as did so many others.

the end

FISHERTON MILL ESTATE, including Harnham Mill, was sold in 1931. The sale document includes 'The Old Bone Mill and four adjoining cottages' (sold for £405 and £375 respectively) promoting the mill as:

this interesting old building known as the Bone Mill is also of considerable antiquity; it has not however been operated as a mill now for many years. Some authorities consider the Building was not originally a mill and that it came to be adapted as such about 1500. It is associated with ecclesiastical power and a reliable authority states that the muniments of the Cathedral at Old Sarum were kept in it during the building of the present edifice. Both mills [Harnham and Fisherton] were driven by water wheels until recent years ....'[21]

Myths endure into the twentieth century.

The 'structure' is described as having been used by tallow chandlers for 'two generations' and to comprise the ground floor 'adapted as a boiler room and store', the first floor store with two loading hatches, and spacious loft. It was let, on a yearly

6 Advertisement for The Old Mill Hotel and Restaurant. (Salisbury Guide 1938)

The Old Mill
Restaurant & Hotel
West Harnham
SALISBURY

Apply the Proprietor.   Telephone : Salisbury 207611

XIIIth Century
Monks' Hostel

Headquarters of
ENGLISH FOLK COOKING ASSOCIATION
(Salisbury Branch).

WILTSHIRE SPECIALITY DISHES.
Morning Coffee.   Candlelight Suppers.

LUNCHEONS : TEAS : DINNERS

Excellent Bath Rooms.

GOOD CAR PARK and LOCK-UP GARAGES.

19 Brown's *Directory of Salisbury* 1925 p 321 and Kelly's *Directory of Salisbury* 1927 p 189
20 See Chapter 4
21 Thake and Taunton p 2

7 The restaurant on the first floor of the mill building, as shown in an advertisement in Salisbury Guide 1938

tenancy to Mr Sangar 'a tenant of long standing'; possibly as long as 52 years if he was the tallow chandler who first took the tenancy in 1879. Water rights were reserved to Fisherton Mill reflecting the interdependence of the two mills on separate branches of the same river.

In the last three-quarters of a century, the two buildings have probably seen more changes than in the whole of their preceding history. The factory was not part of the Fisherton Mill estate and hence not sold in 1931. By 1938 the two buildings were linked, and were using the already by then hackneyed mythical early identity as a monks' hostel in advertising for trade.[22] The advertisement is shown in Figure 6 and reveals that The Old Mill Hotel and Restaurant was the headquarters of the local branch of the English Folk Cooking Association, and proud of its bathrooms, possibly a novel feature in a small country hotel at the time. The restaurant appears to have been on the first floor of the mill, Figure 7 shows it open to the roof.

Forty years earlier a local directory listed the City Rowing and Sailing Club using a 'capital stretch of water from the Bone Mill at West Harnham to Bemerton' by kind permission of H P Gregory Esq.[23] Did the club continue to flourish, and its members enjoy refreshments at the hotel? In 1897 the mill had of course turned to tallow, but the old name was firmly etched in local memory, remaining so at the time of the 1931 sale and long after.

There is some anecdotal recollection that during the Second World War the 'factory' was a hostel – possibly requisitioned – providing accommodation for workers at Wellworthy's engineering plant on

22 *Salisbury Guide* published for the Corporation by the Health Resorts Association (G W May Ltd)1938

23 Langmead and Evans' *Directory of Salisbury* 1897 p 43

Harnham Road where parts were being produced for Spitfire aircraft in Southampton. Post war use is hazy, at one stage the mill was a pottery, marked as such on the 1972 Ordnance Survey map; there was a kiln where part of the hotel kitchen now stands.

Other long local memories tell of the mill, though are often not consistent. Three will suffice. Older residents with recall to the 1920s can remember the overpowering stench of animal carcases on their way to the tallow factory; one gentleman recalls, in the 1940s peering down into the mill race inside the building, not then walled in the same way as now; and some remember as children in the 1970s buying trinkets from the gift shop and tearoom – tea and cakes but only from 11.00 until 2.30pm – run by a Norwegian couple.

Finally, do not be fooled by the mill-stone embedded in the outside of the kitchen wall; it is pure decoration, in no way connected to the many functions of the mill over the centuries.

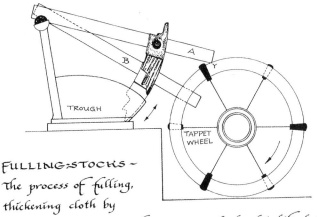

8 A modern reconstruction of a pair of fulling hammers operated by a wheel; note that the hammers slide down the inner side of the trough in order to push and circulate the cloth (Vince, reproduced with author's permission)

FULLING-STOCKS ~
The process of fulling, thickening cloth by pounding, made use of a tappet wheel. This lifted the fulling stocks A+B as it revolved - three times at each revolution. When each tappet reached y the stock could fall into the trough containing the cloth.

2
Cloth

Six huge Fulling Hammers, which interchangeably
Thumping several Pieces of Cloth, made the terrible Noise that caus'd
All Don Quixote's Anxieties and Sancho's Tribulation that Night

Don Quixote, Cervantes 1605

Celia Fiennes, traveller

MANY EARLY WRITERS comment on the noise of a fulling mill and Celia Fiennes (born at Newton Tony only a few miles from Harnham), travelling in the 1690s describes the processes and the frightening machinery

.... I was an eye witness…then they lay them [the woven cloths] in soack in urine then they soape and soe put them into the fulling-mills and soe worke them in the mills drye till they are thick enough, then turne water into them and so scower them; the mill does draw out and gather in the [cloths], it a pretty diversion to see it, a sort of huge notch'd timbers like great teeth, one would think it should injure the clothes but it does not, the mill draws in with such violence that if one stands neere it, and it catch at your garments it would be ready to draw in the person even in a trice; when they are thus scoured they dry them in racks strained out, which are as thick set one by another as will permit the dresser to pass between and huge large fields occupiy'd this way all round the town .... then when they burle them picking out all the knots, then fold them with a paper between each fold and so sett the iron plaite and screw down the press on them, which has another iron plaite on the top under which [there is a] furnace of fire of coales, this is the hot press; then they fold them exceeding exact and then press in the cold press ... [24]

Salisbury's cloth industry

BETWEEN ABOUT 1300 and 1600 the English economy was dominated by wool, either in that raw form or woven into various types of cloth. As New Sarum grew from its inception in the mid twelfth century to become one of the country's major cities its merchants with their 'forceful cosmopolitan ways' were wealthy and powerful. Cloth manufacture developed as a major industry from about 1350. Locally the industry faded by the end of the sixteenth century but had a strong though short revival in the eighteenth. Celia Fiennes is writing in a wider context – the quotation above relates to Exeter – but her description is valid for Salisbury's cloth industry both in its medieval phase and later. [25]

There is sometimes confusion about the sources of wool during the earlier and later periods. During both, this raw material was provided locally and also imported from a wider area. However from the mid sixteenth century a particular breed, the Wiltshire Horn, appeared especially suited to the sheep/corn system that dominated the agriculture and economy of the chalk valleys around Salisbury. Eighteenth and earlier nineteenth century writings about vast numbers of sheep on Salisbury Plain and the Downs are describing Wiltshire Horn flocks which had nothing to do with the cloth industry. A Wiltshire Horn did not produce wool and is described as having 'a thick, matted covering of hair more like a horse or beast [as in oxen or cattle], with a little wool that peels as the animal fattens'. The modern breed society promotes them as the woolless meat sheep.

Harnham's contribution

CLOTH WORKING involved the wool in a production line, a succession of cottage industries or outworking operations at different locations – grading, cleaning, carding with teazles, spinning, weaving, fulling, stretched by tentering, napping and dyeing. All the processes were essential but the two most complex were weaving and

24 Morris p 246 (transcription of Fiennes)
25 Chandler ch 3; Newman and Howells ch 3; Purvis ch 4 and 5

fulling. The first can be illustrated briefly; the latter with which the local mills were involved, in more detail.

Weaving as a cottage industry is illustrated in the probate inventory of Samuel Bayly, a wealthy resident of Marlborough in the seventeenth century. Listed in his shop were:

> Two loomes and harness, one warping barr, two skarms, three tourns, two [blank] and scales … One rack and posts that the cloth is racked in Elsewhere in the house were furnaces, a 'hott press', horse cloths, linseys, linen yarn, brown linsey, druggett, a stock of wool and 'two hundred and fifty pounds woollen yarn at nine pence the pound – £9 7s 6d.[26]

Harnham and other local mills were concerned with fulling, and possibly some of the processes which followed as described in a somewhat impressionistic way by Celia Fiennes above. In the published record of her travels she includes descriptions of developing industries. Fulling was well developed by her time and changed little between the thirteenth and nineteenth centuries. What her writing does tell us is that those who conducted the water powered fulling might also go on to complete the processing.

This seems possibly to have happened at Harnham, at least during its second manifestation as a fulling mill. Immediately behind the mill is an extensive area shown on the 1787 Inclosure Map as Rack Mead, a typical name for an area used for tentering, or stretching the cloth on 'racks'. Rack Mead was also part of the irrigated water meadow system that was a feature of the sheep/corn system and may not have been wholly devoted to tentering racks. A small area behind the mill was shown in the 1931 sale document (back cover) as Lot 10 in the same ownership as the mill and this is more of a size that would have served its output. There is documentary reference to Harnham in 1299 but not again in a fulling context until 1753.[27]

the processes

THE EARLY FULLING PROCESS involved men treading the woven cloth in wooden tubs of stale urine. Where water power was handy it was harnessed to this process at watermills in the vicinity.

26 Williams and Thomson (eds) *Marlborough Probate Inventories 1591 – 1775* Wiltshire Record Society Vol 59 entry 351
27 Rogers p 5 and p 254

9 *When Harnham's paper mill reverted to fulling in the eighteenth century the competition it faced was equipped with large machines far bigger than it could accommodate as shown in these various views.*

Top, a diagram published in 1773 of 'driving' stocks of a size and structure for which Harnham might have had space. However much bigger machines had been developed on the continent as illustrations as early as 1607 show. That at bottom left, shows six pairs of hammers operated from a shaft and that on the right two hammers operated by a shaft geared to an external waterwheel - the size here is indicated, probably exaggerated, by the figure carrying cloth in the bottom left corner. Note that the actual drop of the hammers is not very great and they are designed to push and circulate the cloth. (top Diderot's Encyclopedie 1773, reproduced in Pelham; bottom 1607, Singer vol III p 414)

However some questioned the usefulness of mills and preferred to stick to tubs. Both options are illustrated.[28]

A 'say' of raw cloth taken from the loom was passed to the fuller – here involving transport from the weaver in the city across Harnham meadows along what is now called Town Path to the mill. The fibres of raw cloth are 'loose, airy and unmeshed' similar in appearance to cheese-cloth or sack-cloth and retaining quantities of oil and grease. It was treated with a solution of ammonia to remove oils and then, in the mechanised process, pounded (with a pushing motion) by heavy wooden hammers in shallow troughs to compact the fibres into a felt. Equally fullers' earth, which absorbs grease easily, could have been used. The hammers were hinged on the opposite side of the trough to the horizontal drive shaft that raised or lowered them in turn by means of tappets.

After fulling came tentering. A tenter frame was a wooden structure, not unlike a fence, with upright posts, a fixed rail along the top and an adjustable one near the bottom. On both bars, every few inches, were L shaped iron hooks, pointing up at the top and down on the bottom rail. This was set to stretch the cloth to the required width. Fiennes describes them as being only so far apart that the 'dresser' can move between them; he used dried teasel heads to raise the nap followed

28   See Figs 2, 4, 8 and 9

10 Tenter-frames at Devizes (Stukeley 1723)

by 'shearing' or 'croppping', trimming surface fibres with very large hand shears. Finally the fulling mill could have the responsibility for folding and passing the cloths through a hot and then a cold press.

the machinery

A T THE TIME OF DOMESDAY all mills were used for grinding corn, converting the horizontal rotary motion of the water-wheel shaft to successive vertical and horizontal shafts and finally to the mill stones and other devices. The potential of the power generated soon led to its application for other purposes by the conversion of the rotary to reciprocating motion – backwards and forwards or up and down. This could operate the wooden hammers used in the mill in the fulling of cloth.

Thirteenth century fulling created the first powered machinery, to work wooden hammers raised by and dropped from tappets on a shaft driven directly or indirectly from a water wheel. They were housed in tiny mills but the same concept was still in use six centuries later in the great industrial cloth mills of the north. And William Langland summed it all up rather well

> Clooth that cometh fro the wevying is noght comely to were
> Til it be fulled under foot or in fulling stockkes
> Wasshen wel with water and with taseles cracched [scratched]
> Ytouked and ytennted and under taillours hande
>   William Langland *Piers the Plowman* 1362

Accounts for building a mill at Marlborough in 1237 record the carpenters making and adjusting *flagella et baterella,* scouring mallet and milling hammers.[29] Paper making later required much the same technique.

By the time of the bone mill in the nineteenth century different machinery was in place and is illustrated (Fig 18). On conversion to a tallow factory, water power was probably not needed although water itself, in large quantities, would have been.

29   Nicholson in Corbett (ed) p 30

3
Paper

Thou hast most traitorously corrupted the youth
of the realm, in erecting a grammar school: and
whereas before our forefathers had no others
than the score and the tally thou hast
caused printing to be used; and, contrary to the king,
 his crown and dignity, thou hast built a paper-mill

Henry VI Part 2 1592

why paper?

NOTWITHSTANDING the apparent *lèse-majesté*, after several centuries as part of Salisbury's cloth industry Harnham's mill was rebuilt in the form we see today to produce paper. Exactly when production started is uncertain but probably well before 1592 when Shakespeare was reflecting the authorities' view that paper and thus literacy was not for the masses.

By 1503 Salisbury's population of 7 – 8,000 made it still a major city – possibly ninth in the national order. But the local cloth trade was beginning to decline as fashions changed and the clothiers failed to respond. No doubt there were those who saw opportunities in redundant fulling mills and paper was a product for which demand would increase. However, the scanty published evidence suggests that as an industry it was slow to grow. In the Salisbury area, apart from Harnham, the only other clear documentary references are much later: to 'Lord Coleraine's paper mill at Nunton' in 1676; and another marked on Naish's 1716 map

of Salisbury, powered by one of the city's drain outflows on to Bugmore.[30] During the first half of the seventeenth century there were 'at least 38' paper mills in England but from then on the number increased to peak at 602 in 1825.[31]

The earliest machines involved in making paper were not dissimilar to those needed to manufacture cloth. There were a series of processes conducted around stamping machines where hammers were lifted and dropped by means of tappets on a drive shaft. An essential difference was that while in cloth-making the various processes might take place at different places all the paper making processes were concentrated in one spot. Later more sophisticated machinery based on the 'Hollander Tub' would supersede the stamping machines, needing more space and driving out the smaller mills. Various examples are illustrated. [32]

11 An engraving published in 1568, earlier than Figure 3, captioned 'The first illustration of a paper-miller at work'. (At rear) water-driven stamp-mill; (centre) press for squeezing sheets; (foreground) vat-man using the mould, while his boy carries away the finished 'post' (Singer vol III p 412)

the stamper process

LARGE SCALE INDUSTRIAL paper making, using imported wood pulp and esparto in factories did not begin until about 1800. For three centuries before that paper was costly, 'hand made' from materials that ranged from linen and cotton rags for the best quality white paper to coarser stuff – poor rags, old ropes, netting, or canvas – to make more common coloured paper for wrapping and packing. Labour intensive processes were involved, most often in water-powered mills. The process was introduced into England in about 1490, perhaps shortly before the time when Harnham Mill was being rebuilt.[33]

Rags had to be washed and sorted, cut into small pieces, placed in a water filled stone tub and macerated ['to soften by steeping'], using

30 Bettey (ed) p 252; RCHM *Salisbury I*, pl.16
31 Shorter (1966) p 6
32 See Figs 11, 12, 13, and 14
33 Modern published descriptions of the whole process tend to vary – especially web sites concerning particular places. Shorter is an authoritative source and what follows is largely summarised from his work.

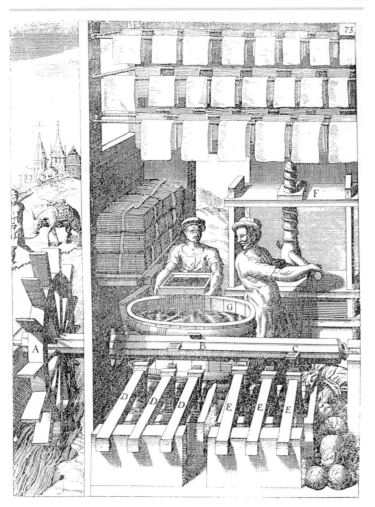

12 *Water Paper Mill of about 1662, operated by tappets on the waterwheel shaft. Unlike cloth fulling, where the hammers push and consolidate the material, the rags for paper making need to be 'macerated' or broken down so these two sets each of three hammers are dropped heavily straight into the tub. All the various processes have been compressed in this illustration. At bottom right bags of rags wait to be sorted and cut into small pieces. On the left the waterwheel drives its shaft to operate the stamping hammers. In the centre pulp is transferred to the vat and successive sheets of paper are lifted in a sieve to assemble the 'post' or alternating pile of paper and felt. These are stacked behind the sieve man, either before or after being drained in the press. Above, the sheets hang to dry and outside a laden donkey plods away (from* Theatrum Machinarum Novum *1662 G.A.Bockler in* Singer vol III p 412)

hammer-like stampers [a device to 'crush and pulverize'] driven by a water wheel and creating a pulp. The resultant pulp was put with water in a vat and kept lukewarm; the 'milky stuff' was agitated by means of a pole. From the pulp the 'vatman' formed a piece of paper by inserting a wire sieve, shaking it to lose surplus water and leave a mat of interlocking fibres on the surface. This was a sheet of paper, now lifted off and placed on a piece of felt so that successive layers of paper and felt built up a multi-layer 'sandwich' called a post. This was placed in a wooden screw press to squeeze out the remainder of the water. The individual sheets of paper were separated and then hung in a drying loft where wind and air currents could evaporate moisture in the paper until it was dry. An illustration from 1662 shows the sheets hung singly in a way akin to washing on a line (Fig 12). It has been suggested that they might also have dried on 'maidens', or 'clothes horses', in front of the fires.

13 'French papermakers of the eighteenth century at work in a factory'. One press is in use, a larger one is being loaded; 'posts' are being pre-pared, the vat-man is busy, and various incidental devices are spread out. A fairly simple mill, and this equipment could have been fitted into Harn-ham Mill, but needed a work force of more than just the miller (Singer vol III p 416)

At Harnham the louvred shutters in the south face and apertures in both gable ends were complemented by fires at both ends of the ground and first floors. The louvres, which shut out rain but allowed passage to the air gave paper mills a distinctive appearance.[34]

the Hollander tub?

THE STAMPER PROCESS took time – 36 hours to fully macerate a single tub of rags is one estimate. This did not meet increasing demand and around 1730 a Dutch innovation appeared, the wooden Hollander tub or beater. A rotating drum ensured the pulp circulated around the tub and bronze bars on both the drum and base ripped the rags. The process has been likened to a modern lawn mower. A number of mills all over England have been identified as flourishing on the basis of this new technology and it has been suggested that during the eighteenth century virtually all the English mills had taken to using these more efficient Hollander tubs.

The configuration of the machinery transferring power from the mill wheel to the drums was different from that needed by the stampers. Pictures show the power transmission and layout for sets of up to six tubs. In the absence of any evidence there can be no knowing whether Harnham Mill benefited from what was probably a more expensive

34 Gregory p 95

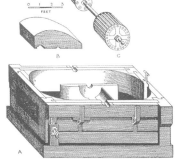

14 (left) 'Manually worked stamp-mill of a simple kind which could be used for beating rags to make paper'. This was a more sophisticated used of tubs and obviously of no relevance to watermills. This illustration is included to emphasise that making paper was initially a destructive process and here heavy vertical stampers when released from their tappets simply dropped into the tubs. (Singer vol III p 413)

16 (below) A modern reconstruction of a Hollander tub with explanatory text (Gregory, reproduced with permission from Phillimore & Co Ltd)

15 (above) The innovation that must have driven small mills such as Harnham out of business was the Hollander tub, introduced on the continent in the late seventeenth century and a more efficient means of production. The explanatory caption is integrated with the early drawing (Singer vol III p 414)

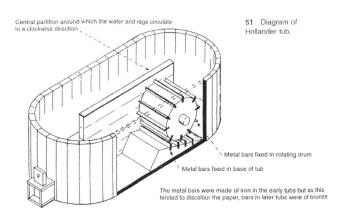

Central partition around which the water and rags circulate in a clockwise direction

51 Diagram of Hollander tub.

Metal bars fixed in rotating drum

Metal bars fixed in base of tub

The metal bars were made of iron in the early tubs but as this tended to discolour the paper, bars in later tubs were of bronze

technology although to do so would clearly have increased production. From the descriptions and especially the illustrations it looks unlikely that it could have adapted; no doubt explaining why paper-making ceased soon after 1700. Also, the 1700 deed[35] refers to stocks and hammers which

35 See page 12

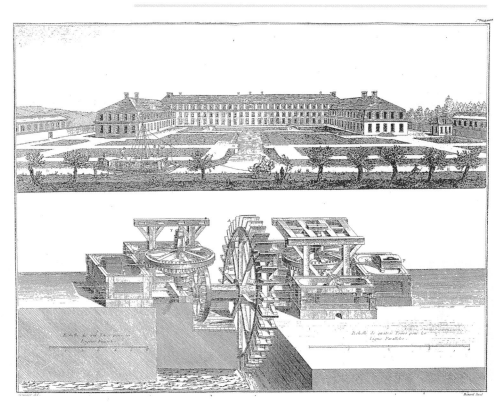

17 *An example of the industrial competition. A large French mill, obviously well established before this illustration of 1767, appears to have two races draining into the canal, and accommodating sets of six tubs. The cutaway diagram shows that each set had a water wheel, pit wheels on either side and bevelled gearing via crown wheels to the drive shaft in each tub. It is not possible to imagine anything remotely of this scale at Harnham: no doubt why it was out of business before 1714 (Diderot Encyclopedie 1767, with acknowledgement to Martin Watts who provided this copy from a facsimile in Exeter University Library)*

suggests the use of Hollander tubs was unlikely. The mill was almost certainly one of the small enterprises that were scattered about making 'common papers' — such as a 'coarse paper useful only for a chapman [a hawker, usually of cheap books] to wrap wares in' until even that faded, and the mill reverted to fulling. And Shakespeare was now promoting paper, regardless of what those in authority might have thought.

He hath not fed of the dainties that are bred in a book ;
He hath not eat paper, as it were; he hath not drunk ink
                                                    Shakespeare *Love's Labour's Lost* 1595

4
Bone and Tallow – and parchment

Where the carcase is, there shall the eagles be gathered together
The Bible St Matthew 24

I T IS PERHAPS UNLIKELY that eagles gathered at Harnham; but scavenging birds seem a very likely consequence of carcases delivered to one or other of the processes carried on there. A single animal carcass provides for all three, bones to be ground for fertilizer, fat to be boiled for tallow, and the hide for parchment. With the arrival of a parchment factory sometime before 1879 within a hundred metres or so of the mill there might seem to have been a synergy. However bone milling may well have stopped sometime earlier than the removal of its machinery in that year. Steamships and railways increasingly carried cheap imported fertilizer during the later part of the nineteenth century and a small, labour intensive, local mill may quite possibly have been forced out before then. Tallow production from 1879 until at least 1931 did broadly coincide with the parchment factory. When parchment making stopped is not clear.

The Parchment Works is identified as such on the 1881 Ordnance Survey map, actually surveyed in 1879, the year when bone gave way to tallow. It is shown as a building along the back of what is now the hotel car park, from behind the Three Crowns public house as far as the water course alongside the yarn factory. It is shown, unidentified, on the map in the 1931 sale brochure and is visible on a 1949 air photograph. The northern end is shown by the Ordnance Survey in 1953 but now there are only slight traces to be seen on the car park wall.

A useful description is given in the *Salisbury Journal* of 8 May 1897 when virtually the whole brick and timber building, and its stock of skins, parchment, and wool was destroyed by fire. The factory was some 100 yards long with an engine house in the middle. The report says that the property was 'properly insured' which no doubt accounts for the fact that Mr Crook was still listed as parchment manager in the 1901 census.

West Harnham, on the face of it a small agricultural village, had during the nineteenth and early twentieth centuries quite an industrial heart. The censuses of 1881 and 1891 include the occupations of skinner, parchment maker, fellmonger, tallow chandler, size maker and leather dresser's assistant. Some lived in Bone Mill Cottages, behind the mill where modern houses now stand.[36]

18 Plan of the ground floor showing the bone crushing machinery in place; drawn from the 1879 contract, superimposed by Howard Austin Jones

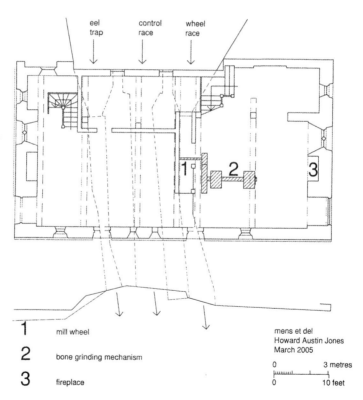

eel trap   control race   wheel race

1   mill wheel

2   bone grinding mechanism

3   fireplace

mens et del
Howard Austin Jones
March 2005

0   3 metres
0   10 feet

36 RG11/2069 f45-46, RG12/1621 f88-91

19 *The mill in 1875, the open loading door and the adult figure seem to indicate that it was still in use as a bone mill, four years before the grinding machinery was taken out and the building entered the final phase of its industrial life as a tallow chandlery (from Daniels and Jones p 11: archive photograph reproduced courtesy of Peter Daniels)*

While two dogs fight over a bone, a third runs away with it
proverb, probably 14th century

A **bone mill** ground or crushed animal bones or 'bone-black'. The latter is burnt bone, the carbonisation of which provided colouring; the residue could still be crushed. Products were either the coarse or fine grained siftings, both used as fertilizer. The plan drawn on the 1879 contract shows a small machine driven by the water wheel. This gives the impression that there are two grinding wheels on a single shaft but in the absence of an elevation it is only possible to speculate. There must have been other devices, as in a corn mill, to feed the grinding machine, to bag the meal, and to hoist sacks to first floor storage. In 1931 the sale document refers to the first floor store with two loading hatches. One of these, open, is seen in an 1875 photograph. Of course by that date the mill might just have been semi-derelict until 1879 when Mr Sangar moved in, the tallow-chandler whose family had become the 'tenant of long standing' by 1931.[37]

37 Thake and Taunton p 17

how inferior for seeing with, is your brightest
train of fireworks to the
humblest farthing candle

Carlyle Essays 1822

A **tallow chandler** makes or sells candles; presumably Mr Sangar did both. Tallow is defined as 'odourless, tasteless waxy white fat, consisting of suet (the hard fat about the kidneys and loins of cattle, sheep and horses)'. It was used chiefly to make candles or soap – cheap tallow candles as opposed to expensive wax ones made from bees-wax; these were the business of a wax chandler. Tallow was obtained by cutting the fatty tissue into small pieces for boiling and then skimming the surface. The best sort of fat for making candles was sheep or mutton. The fat was melted in a pot over the fire and a wick, made of hemp, linen or cotton, was dipped in and out, the more dips then the bigger the candle.

It is possible that Mr Sangar also made soap, particularly as the market for candles must have diminished in the twentieth century. At Harnham in 1879 a single 'copper' was to be installed under the eastern fireplace on the ground floor; when the building was sold in 1931 this was a 'Boiler room and store 54ft wide by 28 ft depth' – the whole of the ground floor. The depth of 28ft demonstrates that what is now the back wall of the restaurant did not exist and the floor was open to the back of the races and the penstocks under the sloping roof.

Is this not a lamentable thing, that of the skin of an innocent lamb should be
made parchment; that parchment, being scribbled o'er, should undo a man

Shakespeare Henry VI part II 1592

Parchment is the processed skins of animals, mainly sheep, goats and calves, that have been prepared for writing; vellum is a finer product from the delicate skins of newly born calves, kids or lambs. An early commentary says 'parchment it must be emphasised is leather manufactured more elaborately' and there is certainly a very extensive literature. To make a sheet of parchment meant, in short, the use of lime baths, or degreasing operations, creating a 'wet pelt' to be stretched on a frame by cords to adjustable pegs to achieve the right tension, followed by scraping and rubbing with pumice.

The Parchment Works first appears in the 1879 survey and had disappeared by 1953. If carcases were delivered to be flayed it is clearly possible that the tallow factory then took them. In its day the mess and smell resulting from both tallow and parchment manufacture must have been appalling.

5
The Mill

More water glideth by the mill
Than wots the miller of

Shakespeare Titus Adronicua 1593

THE LONG LOW MILL BUILDING, on roughly an east-west alignment, is dated as early Tudor, about 1500, on the basis of its architectural style, by the Royal Commission for Historic Monuments (England), as discussed above.[38] Judging by its design and layout there is also the near certainty of its having been built as a paper mill. Replacing the fulling mill which must have stood previously on or very near the site was an expensive undertaking in the expectation of growth in a new market for paper. This was a significant investment for someone.

The structure is described by the RCHM(E) as 'of two stories with attics, the walls mainly of chequered flint and ashlar [squared hewn stone] and with a tile covered roof'. The two most visible external faces are the south, flanked by the footway and the east, seen as the path turns left between the mill and Island Cottage; both faces are elegantly symmetrical. The formal and technical descriptions of these are

> In the S. front the lower storey has two original doorways and all with hollow-chamfered two centred heads and continuous jambs in square, casement-moulded surrounds under moulded labels with returned stops. Two small loops with chamfered ashlar surrounds between the doorways are of uncertain purpose but evidently original. The wall has a chamfered plinth;

38 See page 5

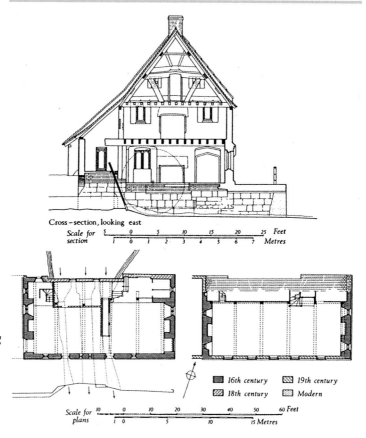

Cross – section, looking east

Scale for section

Feet

Metres

20 *Harnham Mill scale drawings published in 1980 RCHM(E) building 578*

16th century   19th century

18th century   Modern

Scale for plans

Feet

Metres

above the windows a wave moulded hollow-chamfered and roll moulded stringcourse is continuous with labels. The brick-faced upper storey of the S. front replaces the louvred timber elevation depicted by Buckler [1803] and Hall [1834]. Presumably the brickwork is of the 19th century. The gabled E. wall is largely original. The lower storey has a blocked doorway similar to those of the S. front and windows of one or two lights as shown on the drawing [Hall]. In the attic storey a shallow recess with a cinquefoil [five leaf] two-centred head below an abraded stone canopy, carved underneath to represent vault tracery is set between two cross-shaped stone ventilation-loops.

This description is misleading on two counts: the east doorway is much wider than either of the two on the south face; and the 'blocked doorway' actually has a window, shown by Buckler (back cover) in 1803. Ventilation loops are easily understood, along with the louvred shutters allowing air to circulate and help the paper dry. The intricately carved recess is an interesting and inaccessible piece of decoration, described

23 This wide doorway in the eastern gable matched that at the western end when the mill was built and was no doubt needed when paper was being produced. Hall's view of 1834 shows it completely blocked and a modern window to light the hotel restaurant has now been inserted (photo Charles Villiers)

21 Eastern gable, a fine example of chequered flint and ashlar. The bottom left feature is also shown in Figure 23 (photo Charles Villiers)

22 From the back showing the three races, low sloping roof with modern lights and a modern footbridge across the leat to connect the two sides of the hotel (photo Charles Villiers)

24 Penstock for the western of the three races, under the rear of the sloping roof (photo Charles Villiers)

25 The 'niche' high on the eastern gable (photo Charles Villiers)

by Hall as imparting 'the additional character of devotional sanctity and retirement'.

Flints in their natural state are small pieces of very hard silica, usually black, usually rounded and often picked up from the ploughed fields. Locally they were a cheap building material, introduced in the early fourteenth century, and on the outer face of a building would be 'knapped' or split to provide a flat surface. As a decorative feature this remains in common use today.

The squared ashlar needed to be brought long distances from a quarry. At Harnham much can be identified as the oolitic limestone from Haslebury, near Box in northwest Wiltshire, some 35 miles in a straight line, much more for the carts having to use tracks across Salisbury Plain five hundred years ago. This stone was being used for repair and new work on the Cathedral at about the same time and the chequered style was fashionable. Locally, early flint and ashlar chequered walling is to be seen at its best on the eastern gable of Harnham Mill, for all that it shows the wear and tear of five centuries. Flint was easily and cheaply come by, stone expensive. The mix created a handsome building and an attractive style that demonstrated some affluence; not quite as much as that of the church or the earlier wealthy medieval city merchants in their stone buildings but enough for a successful businessman about to embark on this new venture of making paper and hoping that the market was really there.

The back or north faces of both buildings can be seen from the garden, reached through the dividing passage; the west gable end of the mill is masked by the newer building, but the lower part can be seen in the passage as having the same openings as the east end. The interior mirror image can be seen inside on all three floors, somewhat masked by internal, non-structural modern walls. Successive illustrations show how the south front changed during the 19th and 20th centuries, from the 1834 louvered shutters of the former paper mill via some alterations that changed loading doors to the neater windows of modern living accommodation.

There were originally four entrances, the two smaller ones in the south face, not at present (2006) in use, the larger one at the east end closed at some stage and the similar doorway in the passage in use as the entrance to the restaurant. The major doorways at either end were clearly intended for use when the paper mill was built and perhaps the eastern one was replaced by a window for the eighteenth century change of function to fulling. Inside the west door there is a short corridor created when some of the ground floor space became part of the living area.

Beyond is the restaurant, revealing the position of the wheel race and, RCHM(E) again,

> a large open fireplace matched by one, now concealed, at the other end: with chamfered jambs and shouldered and chamfered stone bressummers [a lintel]. Corresponding fireplaces in the upper storey are somewhat taller and have cambered bressummers. The original first-floor windows have oak inner lintels.

26 The iron grids are lead-sealed into the stone surrounds (photo Charles Villiers)

Four large fires and the effect of the louvred shutter and 'ventilation loops' in both gables on all three floors created the right environment for making, and particularly drying, paper. Extending back from the east end is a modern single story brick hotel kitchen where the kiln was in the days of the pottery.

Sangar's 'boiler room and store' sold in 1931 was 54ft by 28ft coinciding with the overall ground plan of the building. Space for the present hotel restaurant is now reduced by various internal walls, not all shown on the plan. The most significant is that separating the machinery (penstocks) controlling the three races. This space is reached from the modern kitchen and under the turn of the eastern staircase. It also serves as the hotel wine cellar! During its working life the whole of the ground

floor was an operating area, as was the first floor with its louvered shutters and loading doors; and possibly the attic roof space.

The first floor is now used for living accommodation and is open to the roof. Part of the space has later twentieth century divisions into rooms with their own ceilings. The formal RCHM(E) description of the roof is:

> .... of five bays, with six collared tie beam trusses with lower angle braces. The cambered collars have been cut to receive the heads of secondary attic doorways and the tie beams are morticed for inserted floor-joists, but the attic floor has gone. There are curved wind-braces to lower purlins.

In the original working form therefore the mill had two open floors and an attic storey divided into a number of rooms. Buckler's 1803 illustration (back cover) appears to show a rooflight towards the eastern end. One of the cut away cambered collars has the remains of the pulley and one of the tie beams has a heavy iron cleat on its side, indicating the presence of one or more manually operated sack hoists. The carpeted living room floor is not accessible but in the ground floor restaurant ceiling a hatch for one hoist can be seen. An illustration in 1938,[39] shows the attic floor removed and the interior of the western gable at the first floor and attic level to be the mirror image of its eastern counterpart – as it is at the ground floor level seen from the passage between the two buildings.

Recalling that the building was constructed as a paper mill, the possible nature of the water powered machinery needed on the ground floor is discussed in the picture captions. Producing sheets of paper and then drying them needed a combination of ventilation and warmth. The former first floor louvered shutters have been replaced by windows but, at each end, the two attic storey cross-shaped ventilation loops remain. None of the external apertures was originally glazed but protected by forged iron grilles sealed into the stone with lead – most of which remain but cover modern glass. The four large open fireplaces created warmth. Those on the first floor are slightly bigger. The two eastern ones are visible in the restaurant and the living room above. Those at the west end are concealed within utility areas.

39 See Fig 7

27 (opposite) The roof: note the tie beams with morticed slots to support floor joists for the former attic ceiling; angled braces can be seen supporting one of the cambered collars cut to receive the heads of attic doorways. (photo Hadrian Cook)

6
The Yarn Factory

The web of our life is of mingled yarn,
good and ill together

Shakespeare All's Well that Ends Well (1603)

THE 1952 LISTING as a Grade I building (Building 1954) refers
to both buildings 'Mill House and the Old Mill (formerly listed as
The Old Mill)'. The description of the mill differs only in unimportant
detail from the later RCHM(E) version although it is worth recognising
that this, in 1952, is the earliest reliable modern description. For this
section the significance lies in the recorded details of the so called 'Mill
House'

> ...a plain 4-storey building to left hand of mill of brick with brick dentil
> [toothed] eaves and hipped slate roof. Originally 2 windows to upper floors,
> now 3. 2 2-light contemporary casements on ground floor with 6-panel door
> lefthand under C18 pediment hood on carved scroll brackets. Service entry
> on right hand side.

The pediment hood thus predates the building and has been moved from
somewhere else after 1834 when Hall's drawing does not show it, or the
door itself. Examples of similar hoods are to be seen in Crane Street and
elsewhere in the city.

There is no evidence that this yarn factory used water power,
although it was elsewhere in similar circumstances. The term 'warehouse'
must have been introduced at some stage and has stuck. More accurately
the building existed in 1818 after Bell and Sutton bought the mill in 1810

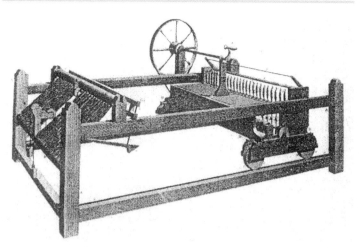

28 *A 'slubbing billy' which pieced together and lightly twisted the short ropes of fibre from the carding machine on to bobbins; this 'slubbing' was then ready for spinning on the 'jenny' or 'mule' (Benson, reproduced with kind permission of Shire Publications Ltd and the author)*

and is then described as a yarn factory. Hall in 1834 (Figure 1) appears to show two windows at the top and four loading doors below; there are no hoisting gantries but one loading platform is half lowered. The two figures on the path are loading packages of sacks which they might well have carried out of the door behind them.

The mill next door had turned to crushing bones by 1840 and so with the final demise of the cloth industry, yarn was possibly no longer an economic product. There is little information about the building from then on as the picturesque mill gets the coverage. Hall dismisses it as 'the square premises beyond ... of modern introduction'. By the mid twentieth century the building had been adapted with modern windows introduced on all three visible sides. There are no known illustrations of the other elevations but the use of the building to house spinning and related machinery suggests that it would have needed to be lit by windows on all sides.

Use as a yarn factory must have involved taking delivery of large quantities of wool in a fairly raw form, possible as 'fells' of fleeces for initial 'scribbling', carding to refine this, and two stages of spinning. Wool might presumably arrive in bulk after shearing and an uncertain number of four different types of quite large machines all had to be accommodated on the four floors. Common sense suggests they were open, and indeed there is no evidence of structural walls to break the space, only timber pillars. Some of the machines that might have been involved are illustrated here.

Although there is no evidence of external gantries or of internal hoists, Hall's 1834 work shows at least one loading door. This and, again, common sense suggest that the heavier dirty processes of cleaning and carding took place on the ground floor, the slubbing was on the first floor, and the nine jennies (large machines with frames of perhaps three by two metres) comfortably filled the two top floors. The relatively light end product, hundreds of bobbins of yarn destined for looms in and around Salisbury were carried down and out to a waiting cart, as shown by Hall.

Today, the ground floor of the hotel building is the bar and reception area with the staircase housed on the east, or right hand side. The original floor plan area of 35ft wide by 28ft has been extended at the back for various utility purposes. The three floors above are divided into guest rooms, back and front, reached by narrow central corridors, together with bathrooms and service areas. The loft space in the roof contains water tanks. There appears to be no remaining internal evidence of the building's former use as a yarn factory.

29 A spinning jenny; some machines could handle more than a hundred bobbins and the manual versions could be operated by women or children in the home. Nine were recorded in the Harnham factory in 1818 together with five other devices. (Singer vol IV p 279)

7
Water

Smooth run the water when it is deepest

Shakespeare Henry VI part II (1592)

THE FUNDAMENTAL PURPOSE of a water mill is to harness the power of the river. Normally this was achieved by channelling the flow of water into a narrow 'leat' and then a narrower 'race' to drive a large wheel. The impact of its rotation had then to be conveyed by means of shafts, gears, belts and pulleys to any device, such as mill-stones for grinding corn or, as here in Harnham, the hammers that pounded cloth or paper.

The plan of Harnham Mill[40] shows three water channels, or races, beneath the ground floor. The first, to the east or the left on the diagram is the wheel race. The second, of unknown purpose, is now called the control race – which may indeed be right because it can be closed or opened to any degree needed to vary the amount of water driving the wheel. Both races seem to be part of the original building. The third race, on the right, was added in about 1808 according to RCHM(E) but they quote no evidence for this statement. Locally it is regarded as having housed the eel trap, a common feature in mills. Judging by the shape of the outlet, its construction is quite different from the earlier two.

It is sometimes said that the river had to be diverted to supply this mill in c1500. That is definitely not so but it is tempting to think that the upheaval of digging a third race under the mill in the early nineteenth century gave rise to this folk memory. The three races can be seen from

40 See Fig 18, p 31

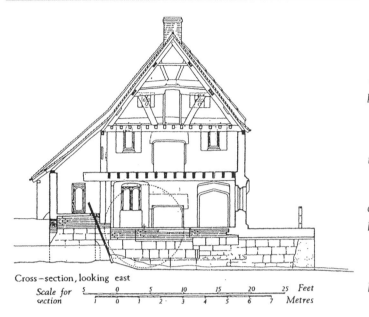

Cross–section, looking east

Scale for section

30 *Harnham mill showing an 11 foot (3.5 metres) diameter wheel and the water flow controlled by an angled penstock. The size of the wheel was constricted by the height of the ground floor ceiling so that the wheel shaft was very close to the floor. To operate either paper or fulling machinery the power of this drive shaft had to be geared via bevelled gears and a crown wheel to a horizontal lay shaft at a height of perhaps 3 feet (one metre). This is illustrated by the cutaway drawing in Figure 17*

the hotel garden. With care, the iron grooves for the hatch plate at the top of each race can just be seen. Water gushing from the outlets downstream adds to the scenic nature of the whole area.

The cross section[41] shows an outline of the undershot breast wheel and, close behind it, the angled penstock, a large wooden board similar to those found in the hatches of the nearby irrigated meadows.[42] The wheel was 11ft (3.5m) in diameter, and some 18 inches (.70 m) wide, fitting tightly between the stone walls of the race. The water line drawn shows very little drop, as a well balanced undershot wheel of this nature requires relatively little water. The other two races have vertical penstocks with the normal rack and pinion device by which they are raised or lowered, similar to those on the nearby meadow hatches, operated by a large iron spanner on the square shaft. The wheel race penstock however is geared to a second shaft turned by a handle and can be finely adjusted more easily. Opening or closing the other races can also help to control the flow onto the wheel. This machinery survives in near working order in the single storey rear extension. The wheel race can be seen from above in the centre of the restaurant. The wheel itself is long gone.

Not all the water was available to the mill. From the early sixteenth century the floors of the chalk valleys were 'floated', or irrigated. Owners

41 See Fig 30
42 Cowan 2005, see index and particularly p 109

and tenants of the water meadows on both sides of the river were entitled to take water at intermittent periods in the winter and spring. This was distributed and then drained back to the river by a series of interlocking carriers and drains. This improved the fertility and value of the grassland. The relatively warm water in spring brought on growth of the grass to provide an 'early bite' for the sheep. These were until the early nineteenth century the Wiltshire Horn breed, rams and ewes both horned, with a coarse coat that they shed naturally in spring and so did not need shearing.[43]

For three hundred years this breed supported the valuable sheep/corn economy. For some weeks in spring they could be walked from the downs to feed on the rich early meadow grass and return to be folded on the arable at night. Early grass meant more sheep could be kept over winter to enrich the arable areas and increase the crop yield. On days when irrigation – or 'drowning' – took place the mill's work was reduced or even stopped. There had to be timetables, agreements and co-operation between the drowners up and down stream, and between drowners and millers. There are documented examples locally of such agreements. At Nunton on the River Ebble in 1676 Lord Coleraine's paper mill shared water with two land owners who took turns each year to use their share first – *alterius vicibus*, to change alternately.[44] From 1849 there is a record at Petersfinger at the junction of the Rivers Bourne and Avon.[45] In the case of Harnham Mill there was also a relationship with Fisherton Mill on the other arm of the Nadder to be taken into account, helped for some centuries until 1931 when they were in the same ownership.

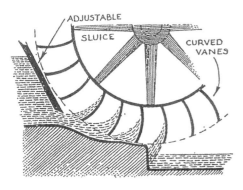

43 Cowan 2005 p 104
44 Cowan 2005, summary page 108, Bettey (ed) 2005, full text page 253 – 5
45 Deed of 1849, information from K Stearne, unpublished.

31 Detail of an undershot wheel (Pancelot's water wheel) of the sort that might have been fitted at Harnham mill; note that the water has only a very short drop to the vanes and that this was enough to power a well balanced wheel. The main water flow is both diverted over the upstream weir and is held back by the penstock. It was the miller's job to adjust the flows so that his wheel was efficiently operated. Here at Harnham there was one, and later two, further races which also had to be taken into the calculation. (Singer vol IV p 203)

8
Around the Mill

A village is a hive of glass
Where nothing unobserved can pass

unknown

THE BOUNDARIES OF WEST HARNHAM reflect those of its medieval origin as a typical chalk valley 'tithing'. This was always roughly square or rectangular to include some of the river valley water meadows, some of the lower downs for arable crops and some of the upper downs for pasture. The farms and other buildings sat just above normal flood level on the 'valley terrace'. Figure 33 is from Ordnance Survey, Wiltshire Sheet LXVI.15, surveyed 1878-9, revised 1900, published 1901;

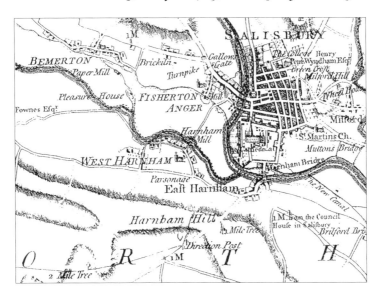

32 Harnham in relation to Salisbury in 1773 (Andrews and Dury)

33 The centre of the village in 1876 (Ordnance Survey, Wiltshire sheet LXVI, 1:2,500)

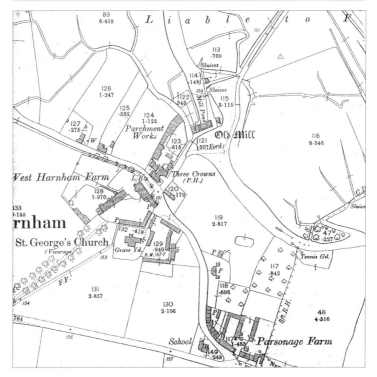

scale 1/2,500. Three digit numbers (eg 128) are plot numbers; the other figure in each plot is the acreage (eg 1.970). These allow a closer examination of the village to which Harnham Mill belonged.

The map shows several trig points or bench marks; 151 feet on the causeway of Town Path (although the meadows on the valley floor are at 150); the middle of the village (by plot 120) is 151; and the ground on which the farm (plots 128 and 129) and St George's Church (plot 132) are a little higher. The terrace rises at the main road near the school (plot 149) to 157 feet. From here, as casual observation, walking or riding a bicycle can easily demonstrate, the steep concave slope rises to the top pastures at 300 feet.

The village had four farms; from the west, Parsonage (plot 117) at the top of Lower Street; West Harnham at the junction of Lower Street, Middle Street and Town Path (plots 128, and 129); Fitzgerald's in Upper Street and Waldrons' Manor Farm slightly further west. The surviving fragments of West Harnham Farm tend to attach the word 'manor' to themselves. Each farm had its own farmhouse and cottages but in the village centre around West Harnham Farm there are more dwellings, no doubt accommodating the work force at the mill and, later, in the yarn factory and parchment works – quite a substantial industrial complex for its time.

The Mill, Yarn Factory and Parchment Works are best identified on the coloured map on the back cover. This comes from the document produced for the sale of Fisherton Mill estate in 1931, and is based on the contemporary Ordnance Survey sheet. The factory is not listed in the sale particulars and seems thus to have been in separate ownership. Lot 10 equates to plot 122 in Figure 33, amounting to just over half an acre, an area of tentering ground that seems intuitively to be adequate for the cloth output that might have been expected from a small fulling mill. However the Inclosure map, drawn over a century before and published when fulling and tentering were still being carried on, shows six and a half acres of Plot 89 as Rack Mead.

Some three hundred yards from the mill St George's Church, the focus of the hamlet, has a Norman nave and chancel, both much repaired over the centuries, and probably stands on a Saxon site. The tower is early nineteenth century and the brick western end is part of a Butterfield restoration in 1874. Opposite the church the thatched cruck cottage was shown on the 1787 Inclosure map as 'vicarage'. The original cottage is now divided in two; there was a mid twentieth century extension to the east and that has itself been altered and extended.

Dozens of generations of Harnham folk lie in the graveyard (plot 132) shown as nearly half an acre but now extended into part of plot 131. Amongst them perhaps are some of the medieval Pynnock family — remember them — and their descendents.

a piece of churchyard fits everybody

anon proverb

Sources

Note that not all these titles are referred to in the text but all have informed its
production

Aspin C *The Woollen Industry* 2006

Benson A P *Textile Machines* 2002

Bettey, J H (ed) *Wiltshire farming in the seventeenth century* Wiltshire Record
Society Vol 57 2005

Bridbury A R *Medieval English Clothmaking* 1982

Brown's *Directory of Salisbury* 1925

Carr D R (ed) *The First General Entry Book of the City of Salisbury 1387-1452*
Wiltshire Record Society Vol 54 2001

Chandler J *Endless Street* 1983

Coleman D G *The British Paper Industry 1495-1860* 1958

Cowan M *Floated water meadows in the Salisbury area* South Wiltshire
Industrial Archaeology Society 1982

Cowan M *Wiltshire Water Meadows* 2005

Daniels P and Garraway Jones T *Then and Now Salisbury* 2003

Gregory R *The industrial windmill in Britain* 2005

Hall P *Picturesque memorials of Salisbury, a series of original etchings and
vignettes, illustrative of the most interesting buildings, and other remains of
antiquity, in that city and neighbourhood, to which is prefixed a brief history
of Old and New Sarum.* 1834

Harnham Women's Institute *A history of Harnham* 1954

Kelly's *Directory of Salisbury* 1927

Morris C (ed) The journeys of Celia Fiennes 1947

Newman R and Howells J *Salisbury Past* 2001

Nicholson R P de B in *A guide to the industrial archaeology of Wiltshire* ed
Corbett 1978

Pelham R A *Fulling Mills* Society for the Protection of Ancient Buildings (SPAB)
undated c1952

Purvis B *Salisbury, the changing city* 2003

RCHM Royal Commission on Historical Monuments *City of Salisbury* vol I
1980

Rogers K *Wiltshire and Somerset woollen mills* 1976

Salisbury Guide published for the Corporation by the Health Resorts Association
1938

Shorter A *Water Paper Mills in England,* Society for the Protection of Ancient
Buildings (SPAB) 1966

Shorter A H *Paper Making in the British Isles* 1971

Singer C *Oxford History of Technology* vol II (1956) vol III (1957), vol IV (1958)

Thake and Taunton, Messrs *Fisherton Mills estate sale prospectus* 1931

Thwaites J R N *The history of the Wiltshire Horn breed of sheep* Wiltshire Horn
     Sheep Society undated but 1990s

Vince J *Watermills and how they work* 1993

Watts M *Water and Wind Power* 2005

Watts M *Watermills* 2006

Williams I L and Thomson S (eds), *Marlborough Probate Inventories 1591 – 1775*
     Wiltshire Record Society Vol 59 2007

34 *The central and widest of the three penstocks with two rack and pinion controls fitted to a square section spindle. It can be raised or lowered with the aid of a massive square headed spanner. The author tries his hand. The cramped area under the low slope of the roof was originally part of the open floor of the mill. It is now walled off from the restaurant and, cooled by the water of the races below, serves as the hotel's wine cellar (Photo, Hadrian Cook)*

Cover Illustrations

Front Cover

On the River Nadder a short distance south west of Salisbury.
The Old Mill Hotel, Town Path, West Harnham SALISBURY SP2 8EU
www.signature-hospitality.com

The early Tudor, two storey stone building on the right was built as a paper mill in about 1500; the earliest such mill now surviving. To the left, the four storey bnck structure was a yarn factory built between 1810 and 1815. The two have been in combined use as a hotel since the mid 1930s. The bridge on the left crosses a 'tail drain' from former irrigated water meadows further upstream (see Chapter 7)

There is a ford immediately downstream from the mill; the two entrances are shown, southern at the top, northern below. The line of the ford from south to north is shown on the coloured map on the back cover (photographs by Charles Villiers)

Back Cover

TOP Harnham Mill, 1803; watercolour by John Buckler (1770-1851).
BOTTOM Centre of West Harnham as shown in the sale particulars when the Fisherton Mill estate was sold in 1931 (Thake and Taunton, map)

The watercolour is one of the four pictures of buildings in Harnham among the 690 drawings made between 1803 and 1812 for *Collections for Wiltshire,* commissioned by Sir Richard Colt Hoare and bound in ten large volumes. They were one of the chief treasures of his library at Stourhead. Hard times in 1916 enabled the Wiltshire Archaeological and Natural History Society to buy the collection, now one its own treasures in the library at the Wiltshire Heritage Museum in Devizes

Buckler was an architect and an authority of the period on medieval architecture. Most of the 690 images are of churches. For the few secular buildings (and this is the only mill) he seemed unconcerned with name or function and captioned this work as *Ancient Building at West Hamham, Wiltshire.* The Society catalogued it (WAM Volume 40, 1917) as *Harnham, West, Ancient Building.* That it was not identified as a mill is perhaps unsurprising as a curator in Devizes was not likely to be aware of the actual building and Buckler does not show the outflows from the races of which, in 1803, there would have been two, not the three now to be seen. His workload and travelling to complete the county wide project in nine years must have been demanding and perhaps some artistic licence is to be expected

The author is particularly pleased to have a rare opportunity, possibly the first, of reproducing this work in colour. *(Reproduced by permission of the Wiltshire Archaeological and Natural History Society)*

Index

Numbers in **bold** refer to illustrations